WITHIN THE GLADE

A collection of poems
written to amuse children
(of all ages)

by

PATRICK MOORE

illustrated by EUAN DUNN

SMH

British Library Cataloguing in Publication Data

A catalogue record for thus book is available from
The British Library

ISBN 978-0-9568591-0-5

First published 2011 by
SMH BOOKS
14 Caen Stone Court, Queen Street, Arundel
West Sussex, BN18 1NG

Typeset by Michael Walsh
The Better Book Company, Chichester

Printed and bound in Great Britain by
Ashford Colour Press, Gosport, Hampshire

DEDICATION

In loving memory of our Mothers:

Gertrude Lilian White Moore

and

Winifred Alex. Simons M Hastie

CONTENTS

FOREWORD

Some time ago, old friends were staying with me, with their two children – a girl aged six and a boy of five. We had been in the garden, watching a Frog leaping about, and they asked me to write a poem about it. I had never written anything of that kind before but I had a go and to my surprise, they loved the Froggy poem. I was challenged to write more, and finally acquired a whole collection ...

Later, other young children seemed to enjoy them, too.

When my friends had gone home, I thought no more about the poems. I forgot about them – until I came across the manuscripts months later, re-read them, and typed them up, on my 1908 Woodstock typewriter.

Then another friend – Sandra Saer – saw them recently, and suggested publishing them, which hadn't occurred to me. I must give grateful thanks to Sandra, without whom the poems would never have seen the light of day.

Well, here they are … See what you think!

Patrick Moore

Patrick Moore
Selsey
4 March 2011

INTRODUCTION

We know Patrick Moore as a great astronomer, author, composer, and performer of no mean talent on the xylophone!

How many people know he is also a poet?

In his Autobiography, when he passed from his sixties to his seventies in 1993, he wrote: *'This did not appeal to me in the least, because there is absolutely nothing to be said in favour of growing old; there ought to be a law against it!'*

Yet old age, although it has its limitations for all of us, has not altered Patrick's many personal attributes: love, friendship, a love to entertain, an unquenchable thirst for knowledge, a love to entertain – and an undimmed sense of humour.

These, in a magical way, are all embedded in his poems, which I am privileged to publish, for everyone to enjoy.

Sandra M H Saer.

Sandra M H Saer
Arundel
2011

THE GLADE

Deep in the woodland glade, you'll find
characters of every kind.
Why not go and see them there?
They certainly won't mind.

Some live in water, some in trees.
But when they feel like company
it's always to be found.

Their weekend parties are a treat,
with song and dance, and much to eat.
So come along, join in the fun –
the latest party's just begun …

1. THE RABBIT

A little rabbit, basking in the sun.
Dark night has ended, day has just begun.
The blackbird trills his morning song of love,
and green leaves cascade down from clouds above.

All nature's wide awake – and it seems funny
to be a gentle, friendly little bunny!

2. THE WEASEL

A clever artist is the Weasel,
With his paint brush and his easel.
Still-life figures are his forte,
Though some of them are rather naughty …
He'll go out every day, quite soon,
And paint right through till afternoon.

So it comes as no surprise
when his pictures win a prize.

3. THE WATER VOLE

The timid little Water Vole
will sometimes leave the comfy hole
he's dug beneath the slender trees
that quiver softly in the breeze.

He'll stroll along the river's edge,
nibbling acorns in the hedge,
but loves the safety of his home
and has no wish at all to roam.

His friends all quickly understand
and think that he is really grand –
a charming, peaceful little soul,
our pretty little Water Vole.

4. THE MOLE

The Mole likes living underground,
because it’s there that cheese is found.
His home is snug, and also bright,
now it has electric light.

His parties are good fun, and gay,
as other Moles will always say,
while folks above can hear the mirth
coming from below the earth.

A friendly creature is the Mole,
happy in his comfy hole.

5. THE SNAIL

Consider now the pleasant tale
of dear old Septimus, the Snail.
He'll breakfast off a leafy fern
and say "Good-morn" to every worm –
asking how they feel today,
and – would they like to come and play?

His shell makes up a splendid home,
and what's inside is all his own.

He may be slimy, that is right,
but Septimus is very bright!

6. THE EARTHWORM

The Earthworm wriggles on and on,
sometimes bursting into song.
His voice is harsh, which is a pity,
but he still sings a cheerful ditty.

When he meets another Worm
they will gladly twist and squirm
and turn themselves into a knot
which, frankly, matters not a jot.

They'll very soon become untied –
just a case of wormish pride.
They will go on, hither and thither,
always with their stately slither.

7. THE NEWT

At water's edge, there lives the Newt
and everybody says he's cute.
He always feels there's much to gain
by giving help, so that's his aim.

His front door bears a note: 'Please enter,
and welcome to our new Health Centre.
Do please sit down now and wait.
I promise you, I won't be late.
And while you all are resting here,
I'll offer you a glass of beer.'

At Medic School, he was well-trained
and so a GP he's remained.
If you are feeling tense and tight,
trust Dr Newt to put you right.
And for all the famous ills
he will prescribe the proper pills.
With syringe, knife and stethoscope,
He'll cure each one, and give them hope.

To make you well, he will endeavour.
And, as we know, he's very clever.

8. THE CROW

I'm very proud to be a Crow,
with many arrows to my bow.
I eat bananas twice a week,
which makes me strong, and look quite sleek.

And yet some people get me wrong.
I say – when bursting into song,
and start by 'cark ing', loud and long –

"You stupid twit, you are mistook –
I am a Crow, I'm not a Rook!"

9. THE EEL

I am a very lively Eel.
I love to dance the Highland Reel.
But living on the river's floor,
my ballroom steps are rather poor.

A waltz, a fox-trot or a jig –
it really matters not a jot!
My partner's soon tied in a knot.
And when the music stops, we find
it takes a while to get untwined.

As a dancer, I'm the dregs –
and all because I have no legs!

10. THE BEAVER

The Beaver always likes to build
and, in this, he's very skilled.
His house is on the river bed
and is unusual, it's said.

Three-storeyed, with a roof of thatch
laid with skill that's hard to match.

The front door is of polished pine,
and everybody says it's fine.
The kitchen is his favourite room.
The joy of cooking makes him boom!

He'll very often say "I feel
it's time I cooked a five-course meal."

And then he contacts all his friends,
with others, on whom he depends,
and says "Tomorrow, come and eat
a meal you'll find it hard to beat."
And when they go home after dinner,
His guests will say "That was a winner!
He's cooked us just what we all like,
so yet again, he got it right.
It really was a cordon bleu.
On that, nobody can demur.

Oh yes, whichever way you look,
the Beaver is a marvellous cook."

HOME
SWEET
HOME

11. THE FIELD MOUSE

The Field Mouse, nesting in the corn,
will slumber there from dusk to dawn.
When morning comes, he will awake
and breakfast off parsnips and cake.
His closest friends will scamper round,
with a little squeaky sound;
they'll paddle in the sparkling dew
in the way that Field Mice do,
gazing at the clear blue sky
and checking that their nests are dry.

It's always good to see the Mice –
and do you know – they're rather nice.

700

12. THE TORTOISE

The Tortoise lives inside his shell.
It is his home – and suits him well.

He moves at his own steady pace,
But what he longs to do is – race.

He'd love to sprint along in style,
and manage a four-minute mile.
"I'll master it at last," he claims,
"no matter what my aches and pains!"

His friends are always very kind,
and say to him "Please, never mind.
No point in feeling sad and sick
because you can't be really quick.

Keep quiet and calm – you have your pride –
so smile, and take it in your stride."

13. THE OWL

The Owl is said to be so wise.

but then we find – surprise, surprise –
that he is really rather dense,
with very little common sense.

> He'll sit upon his branch and hoot
> as loudly as he can, to boot.
> He keeps the other birds awake,
> until they call: "For goodness sake!
> Please don't make that awful row.
> It's nearly time for breakfast now.
> We want to eat our toast in peace,
> so we'll be glad if you will cease."

But he will go his own 'sweet' way,
whatever other birdies say.
A disagreeable old owl,
his mood is very often foul.

14. THE SWAN

The Swan is such a stately bird.
He's fond of beetroot, so we've heard.
His beak is long and sharp and yellow.
His singing voice is deep and mellow.

Operetta is his forte,
though some parts of it are naughty!

He has to stop when it is dark,
even when he's singing Bach;
but when the sun is in the sky
he'll warble on – he's never shy.
He's at his best when singing Verdi –
A very clever, songful birdie.

15. THE RAT

I am a very friendly Rat,
always ready for a chat.
Yet when I start to build a nest,
most people say "You are a pest!"

I think this is a crying shame.
And I hope that all of you
will shortly take a different view.
I merely want to stay at home
and practise on my xylophone.

It's not my fault that I'm a rat –
Nature's taken care of that!

16. THE OTTER

When morning dawns, the graceful Otter
goes for his pre-prandial* potter.
Cabbage is his favourite snack,
and then, there is no turning back.
He's very good at catching fish
and finds they make a tasty dish.

When breakfast's done, he'll take a walk
to see the little Sparrow-hawk.
They have been friends for many years,
and get on well, so it appears.

They sing duets and, as a starter,
always choose a nice cantata.
To show that there is nothing wrong,
they follow with a rousing song.

Their voices blend together well,
as their listeners can tell,
and all the other Otters say
"What a splendid way to start the day!"

*pre-breakfast

J.S. BACH

17. THE THRUSH

The amiable little thrush
will always say "I never rush.
That is just not my concern.
I'll breakfast early, off a worm,
and when I think to take a rest,
I'll go back to my leafy nest.

I'm always glad to spread the word
as I'm sure you must have heard.
Parties in my treetop home
are both lively and well-known.

So come in for a friendly chat –
we'll talk of this, and maybe that!"

18. THE SKUNK

Down in the wood, in a large tree trunk,
there lives a most gregarious skunk.
He will protest: "Don't get me wrong,
it's incorrect to say I pong.
My house is hoovered every day
at half-past seven, come what may.
My kitchen, I keep spick and span,
ventilated by a fan.
My friends all know it very well,
and say it has a lovely smell.

So let me stress, I'm not a punk,
I am a most hygienic skunk."

19. THE FROG

I know a friendly little Frog.
His home is down beside the pond.
He hops around the field all day,
collecting seaweed on the way.

His body is a brilliant green,
as vivid as I've ever seen.
He's never felt the need to smoke
yet somehow has this noisy croak!

He doesn't mind the winter fog.
He is a quite delightful Frog.

20. THE DUCK

The Duck likes swimming on the pond,
eating crisps, of which she's fond.
Flapping her wings, she'll always try.
She thinks it would be nice to fly.

At every flap, the other quackers
shake their heads and say: "You're crackers!
Ducks are safer on the ground,
that's what we have always found.

So kindly do not make a fuss,
and be content to stay with us."

21. THE SQUIRREL

The Squirrel is an acrobat,
all his friends agree on that.
His nest is in a lofty tree,
perched on high, for all to see.

Any creature passing by
will drop in, for a quick mince pie.

He has a long and bushy tail –
when jumping, it becomes a sail.

He's very quick and very agile,
and always ready with a smile.

He's popular with all concerned,
As every woodland dweller's learned.

22. THE NIGHTJAR

The Nightjar doesn't like the day,
and seldom sees the sun.
But when night falls upon the earth,
he starts to have his fun.

He has a very comfy home,
built entirely on his own,
and in it, he's installed a bar
for visitors, from near and far.
Sherry is his favourite drink,
so the rooks and sparrows think.
But the eagle says: "No fear!
I'm coming for my usual beer!"
The Squirrel, bushy-tailed and frisky
much prefers a glass of whisky,
while the Chaffinch thinks it's fine
to have a lot of rosé wine.

It is a very friendly club.
For night-life here, it is the hub.
It is the Nightjar's modest boast
that he is the perfect host.